Clever Cat at the Seaside

Pupil & teacher duets to enhance the early stages of learning
Muntere Schüler-Lehrer-Duette für den frühen Klavierunterricht

Mike Cornick

Illustrations by Wendy Sinclair

UE 21464
ISMN M-008-08041-8
UPC 8-03452-06403-9
ISBN 978-3-7024-6684-8

Cover design: Lynette Williamson
Printing: Plöchl, Freistadt (Austria) – printed using 100% renewable energy

CD recorded at Simon Painter Production, Surrey, U.K. August 2008
Recording engineer and vocals: Simon Painter
CD manufacturer: kdg, Elbigenalp (Austria)

Preface

Clever Cat at the Seaside is intended for slightly more advanced pupils than *Clever Cat*, the first volume in this series, although it is hoped that it will prove to be accessible to those who are still in the early stages of learning.

Once again, the principle of learning through imitation has been adopted in this second volume and, consequently, almost everything played by the pupil in each of these duets is first played in a different octave by the teacher.

Although some pieces address the development of specific skills, the main emphasis here has been to provide enjoyable and descriptive pieces which can be used in lessons and for concert performances. For the most part, the range of keys has been restricted to C, F and G majors and their relative minors, and where this range is exceeded, the piece has been written without the use of a key signature.

Wherever possible:

- Conventional fingering has been suggested although teachers may wish to provide alternatives.
- In the teacher's part, phrases which are to be copied by the pupil are notated in grey and a suggested fingering indicated.
- Although the printed copy is not central to the learning process in this instance, the pupil's pages have been notated at actual pitch except where this would lead to excessive use of ledger lines.

Clever Cat at the Seaside should be regarded as a flexible set of materials and teachers should feel free to modify the pieces as they see fit.

Finally, although the principal use of this book will be in the context of the piano lesson, a CD has been included which contains an enhanced performance of each duet together with a play-along practice track for pupils to use at home.

Mike Cornick
March 2008

Vorwort

Clever Cat at the Seaside richtet sich an etwas fortgeschrittenere Schüler als *Clever Cat*, der erste Band dieser Reihe. Ich hoffe freilich, dass es auch denjenigen Zugang bietet, die sich noch im Anfängerstadium befinden.

Auch in diesem zweiten Band geht es um das Prinzip des Lernens durch Nachahmung. Folglich wird alles, was der Schüler in jedem dieser Duette spielt, zuvor in einer anderen Oktave vom Lehrer gespielt.

Zwar widmen sich einige Stücke der Entwicklung besonderer Fähigkeiten, doch liegt mein Hauptanliegen darin, unterhaltsame und Geschichten erzählende Stücke zur Verfügung zu stellen, die sich für den Unterricht und für die Bühne eignen. Die meisten Stücke beschränken sich auf die Tonarten C-Dur, F-Dur und G-Dur mit den entsprechenden Molltonarten. Wo dieser Rahmen überschritten wird, trägt das Stück keine Generalvorzeichen.

So weit möglich

- wurden konventionelle Fingersätze vorgeschlagen, die mancher Lehrer durch eigene Vorschläge ersetzen wird.
- sind in der Lehrerstimme Phrasen, die der Schüler nachspielen soll, grau gedruckt und mit Fingersätzen versehen.
- wurden die Schülerstimmen in tatsächlicher Tonhöhe notiert, außer wenn zu viele Hilfslinien verwendet werden müssten, obwohl das gedruckte Notenbild in diesem Stadium nicht wesentlich für den Lernprozess ist.

Clever Cat at the Seaside möchte als flexible Materialsammlung angesehen werden, die Stücke können und sollen daher nach Bedarf angepasst werden.

Obwohl dieses Heft hauptsächlich für die Benutzung im Rahmen des Klavierunterrichts gedacht ist, liegt eine CD mit einer Vollversion jedes Duetts sowie einer Play-Along-Version zur Lehrerstimme bei, damit SchülerInnen die Möglichkeit haben, auch alleine im Duett-Kontext zu üben.

Mike Cornick
März 2008

Préface

Clever Cat at the Seaside s'adresse à des élèves légèrement plus avancés que le premier volume de la série, *Clever Cat*, tout en restant – nous l'espérons – toujours à la portée des pianistes qui en sont encore à leurs premières phases d'apprentissage.

Ce second volume obéit, comme le premier, au principe de l'apprentissage par imitation. Dans toutes les pièces par conséquent, presque tout ce que joue l'élève est d'abord interprété par l'enseignant à une octave différente.

Bien que certains morceaux visent à développer des compétences spécifiques, le premier but du recueil est d'offrir des pièces divertissantes et descriptives pouvant être utilisées en cours comme en audition. Elles sont presque toutes écrites en do, fa ou sol majeur ou leurs relatives mineures ; dans le cas contraire, aucune altération n'est indiquée à la clé.

Chaque fois que possible,

- des doigtés classiques sont suggérés, l'enseignant restant libre de proposer d'autres solutions.
- dans la partie jouée par l'enseignant, les phrases que l'élève doit reprendre sont notées en gris et assorties d'une indication de doigté.
- bien que la partition imprimée ne soit pas essentielle au processus d'apprentissage dans le cas présent, la partie de l'élève est notée à la hauteur réelle, sauf lorsque cela supposerait un recours excessif aux lignes supplémentaires.

Clever Cat at the Seaside est conçu comme un support de cours flexible : les professeurs ne devraient pas hésiter à modifier les pièces à leur convenance.

Enfin, bien que le recueil soit avant tout destiné aux cours, il s'accompagne d'un CD comprenant une version enrichie de chaque pièce et des plages d'accompagnement permettant à l'élève de travailler à la maison.

Mike Cornick
Mars 2008

Contents · Inhalt · Table des Matières

The Rockpool 8
Der Gezeitentümpel • Le Pool Rock

The Boat Trip 10
Die Bootsfahrt • Voyage en bateau

Watching the Waves 12
Wellen beobachten • En regardant les vagues

Reggae Dancing: At the Beach Barbecue 14
Grillparty und Reggaetanz am Strand • Barbecue et reggae sur la plage

The Brass Band 1 16
Die Blaskapelle 1 • La fanfare 1

The Brass Band 2 18
Die Blaskapelle 2 • La fanfare 2

The Helter-Skelter 20
Hals über Kopf • À toutes jambes

On the Ghost Train 22
Im Geisterzug • Le train fantôme

The Donkey Ride 24
Der Eselsritt • Balade à dos d'âne

The Deep Blue Sea 26
Das tiefblaue Meer • Profondeurs marine

On the Carousel 28
Auf dem Karussel • Tour de manège

At the Aquarium 30
Beim Aquarium • Visite de l'aquarium

The Echoing Caves 32
Das Höhlenecho • L'écho dans les grottes

Into the Cold, Cold Waves 34
Hinein ins kalte Wasser! • Baignade en eaux froides

Candy Floss 1 36
Zuckerwatte 1 • Barbe à papa 1

Candy Floss 2 38
Zuckerwatte 2 • Barbe à papa 2

Candy Floss 3 – For the More Adventurous 40
Zuckerwatte 3 – Für die Mutigen •
Barbe à papa 3 – Pour les plus courageux

Candy Floss 4 – For the More Adventurous 44
Zuckerwatte 4 – Für die Mutigen •
Barbe à papa 4 – Pour les plus courageux

Dance of the Marionettes 48
Tanz der Marionetten • Danse des marionnettes

The Rockpool

Der Gezeitentümpel · Le Pool Rock

Quaver and semiquaver rhythms • Achtel- und Sechzehntelrhythmen • Rythmes en croches et doubles croches

The Rockpool

Der Gezeitentümpel · Le Pool Rock

Track 1/2

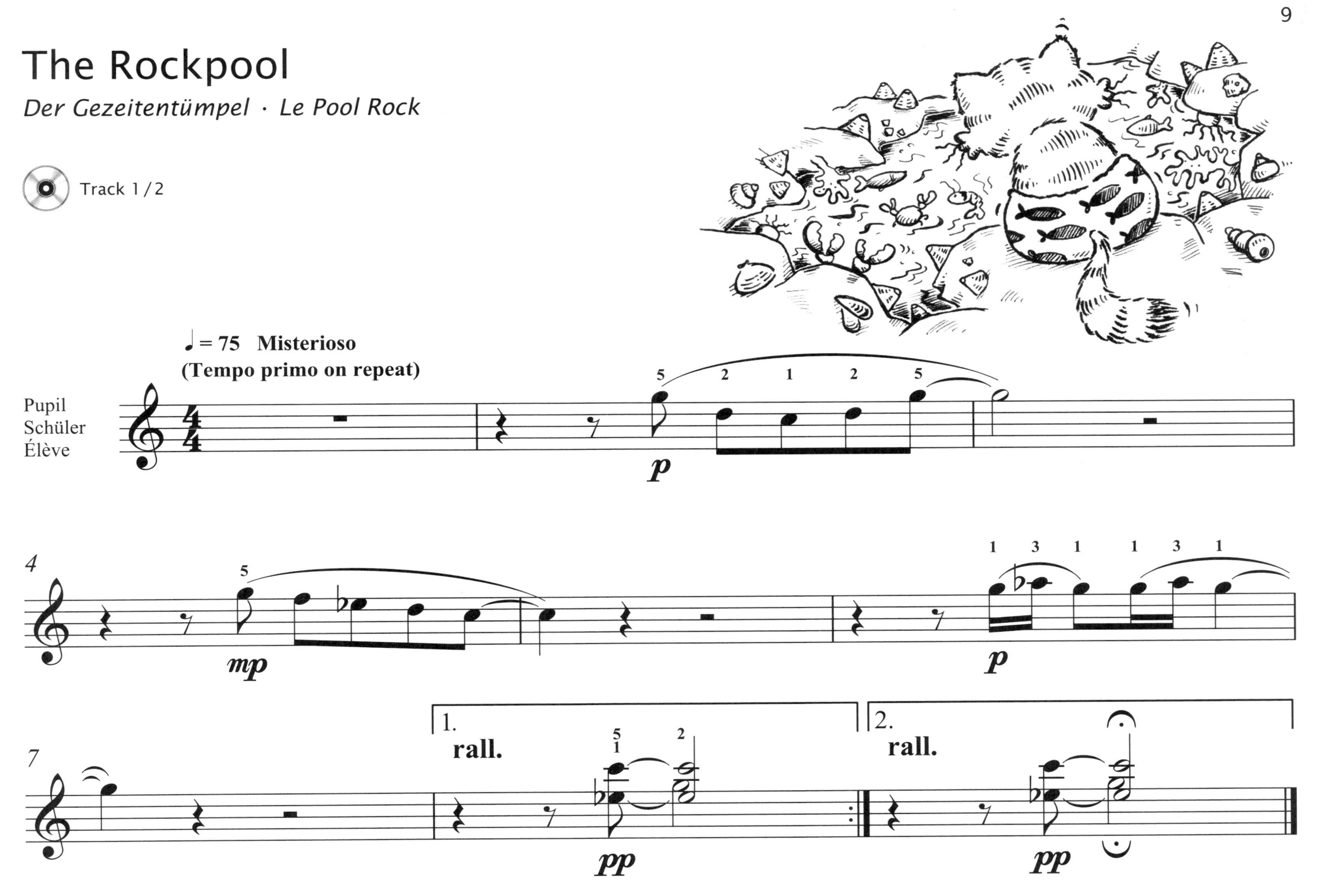

The Boat Trip

Die Bootsfahrt · Voyage en bateau

Track 3/4

The Boat Trip

Die Bootsfahrt · Voyage en bateau

Dotted quaver rhythms and semiquavers • Punktierte Achtelrhythmen mit Sechzehnteln • Rythmes en croches pointées et doubles croches

Watching the Waves

Wellen beobachten · En regardant les vagues

Swing quavers • Swingachteln • Croches swinguées

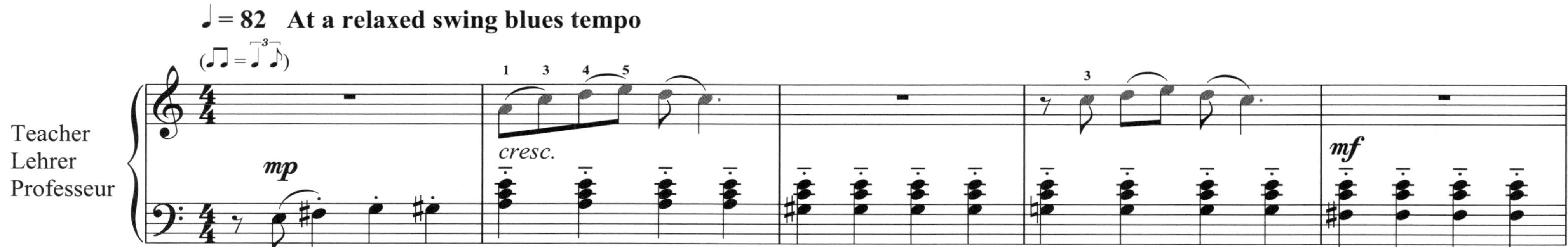

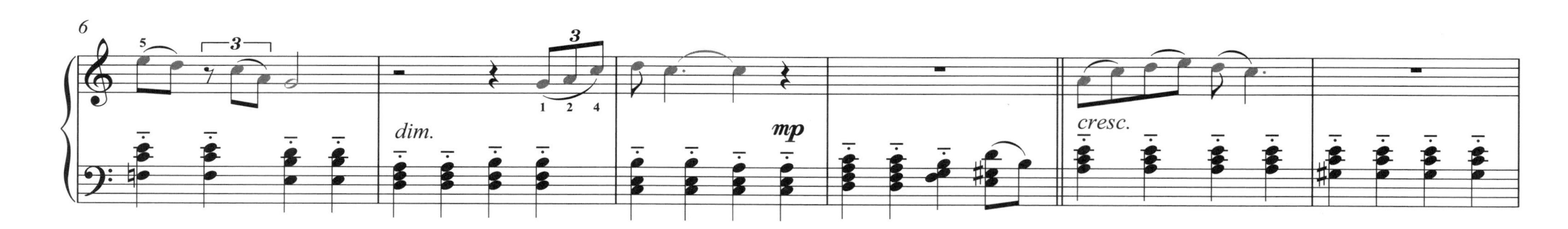

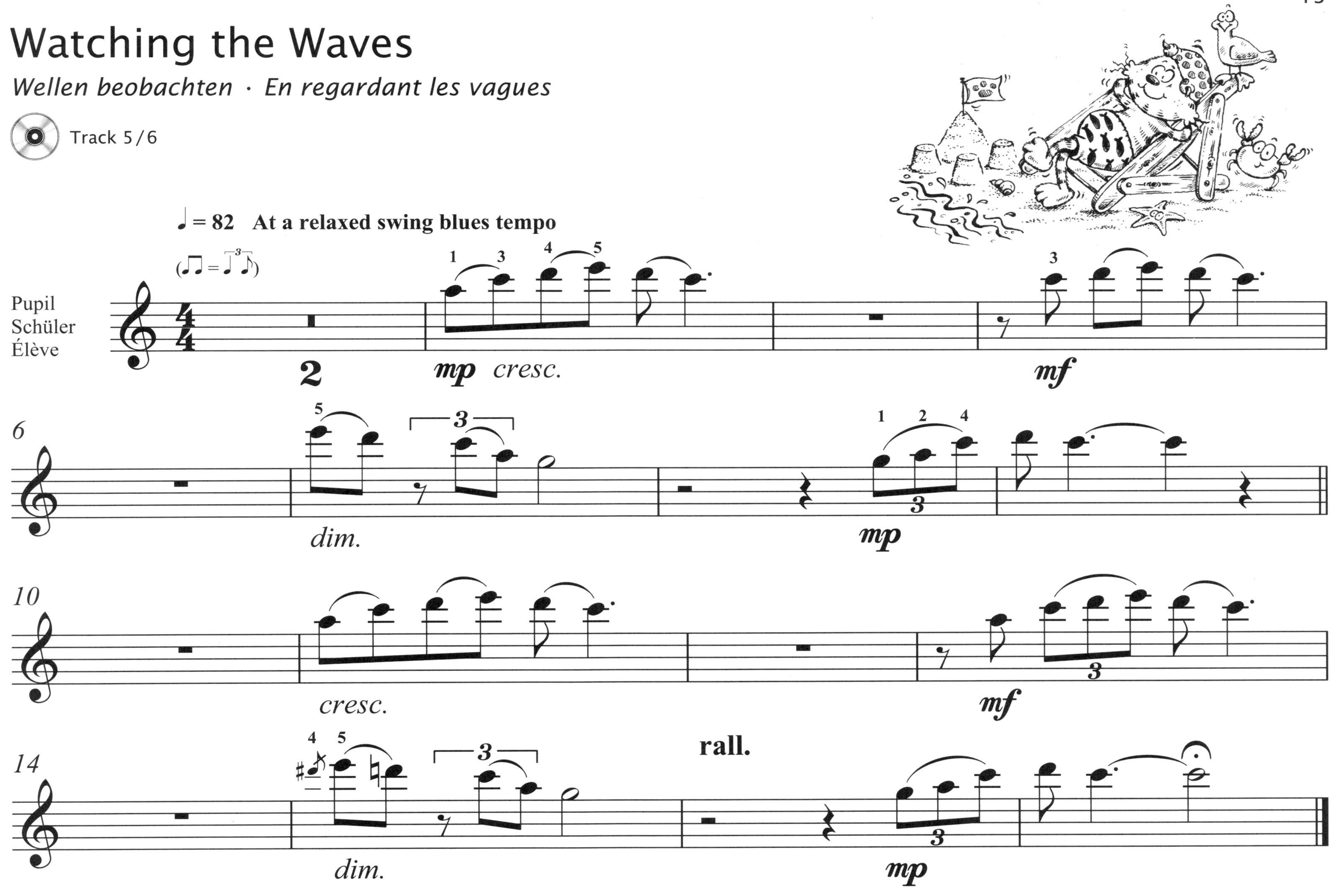
Watching the Waves
Wellen beobachten · En regardant les vagues
Track 5/6
♩ = 82 At a relaxed swing blues tempo
Pupil
Schüler
Élève
mp cresc.
mf
dim.
mp
cresc.
mf
dim.
rall.
mp

Reggae Dancing: At the Beach Barbecue

Grillparty und Reggaetanz am Strand · Barbecue et reggae sur la plage

Reggae Dancing: At the Beach Barbecue

Grillparty und Reggaetanz am Strand · Barbecue et reggae sur la plage

Swing quavers • Swingachteln • Croches swinguées

The Brass Band 1

Die Blaskapelle 1 · La fanfare 1

Swing quavers • Swingachteln • Croches swinguées

The Brass Band 1

Die Blaskapelle 1 · La fanfare 1

Track 9/10

The Brass Band 2

Die Blaskapelle 2 · La fanfare 2

Track 11/12

The Brass Band 2

Die Blaskapelle 2 · La fanfare 2

Swing quavers • Swingachteln • Croches swinguées

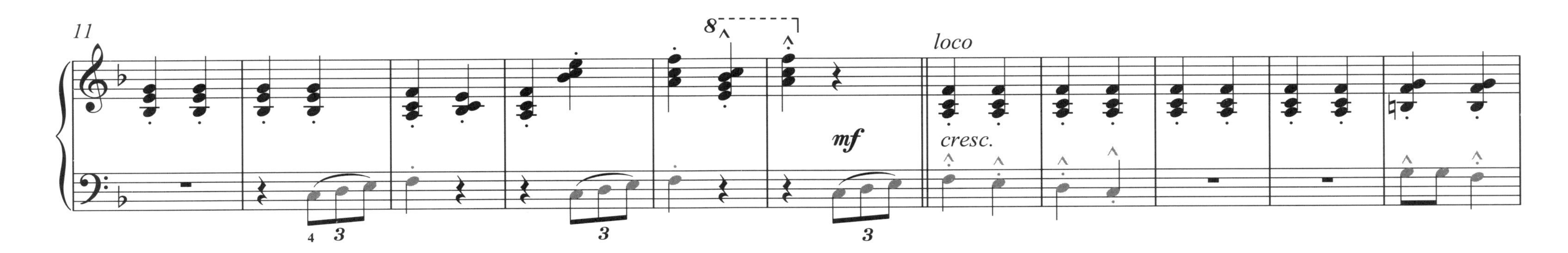

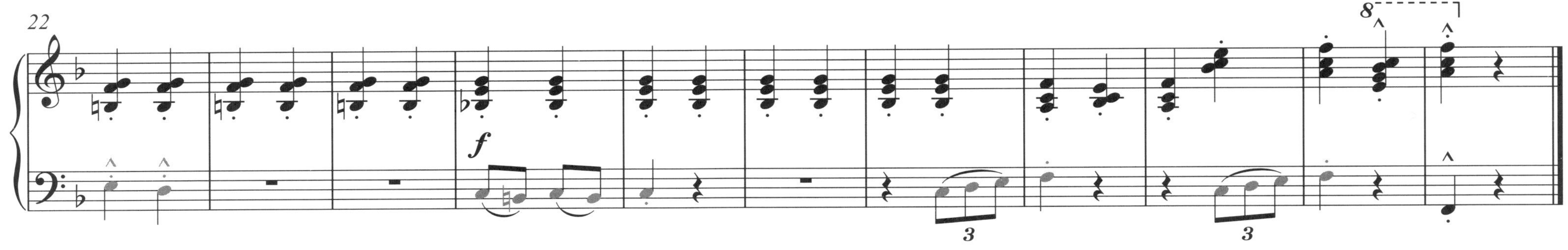

The Helter-Skelter

Hals über Kopf · À toutes jambes

Arpeggios and chromatic phrases • Dreiklänge und chromatische Phrasen • Arpèges et chromatisme

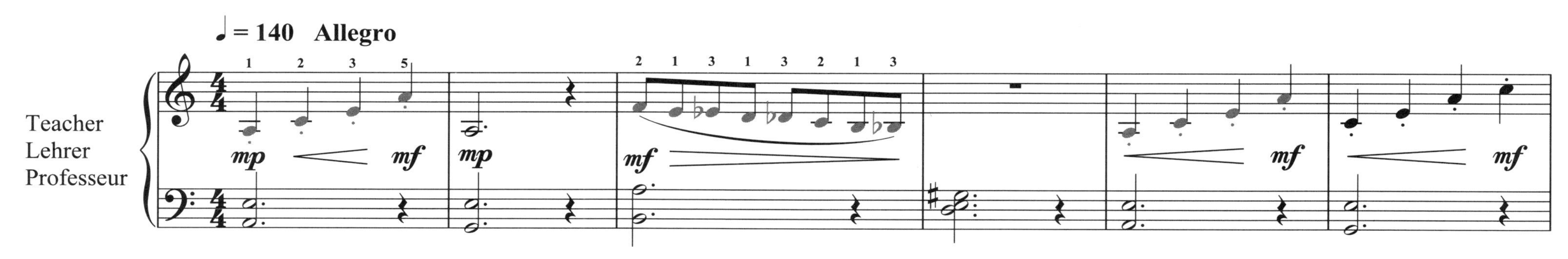

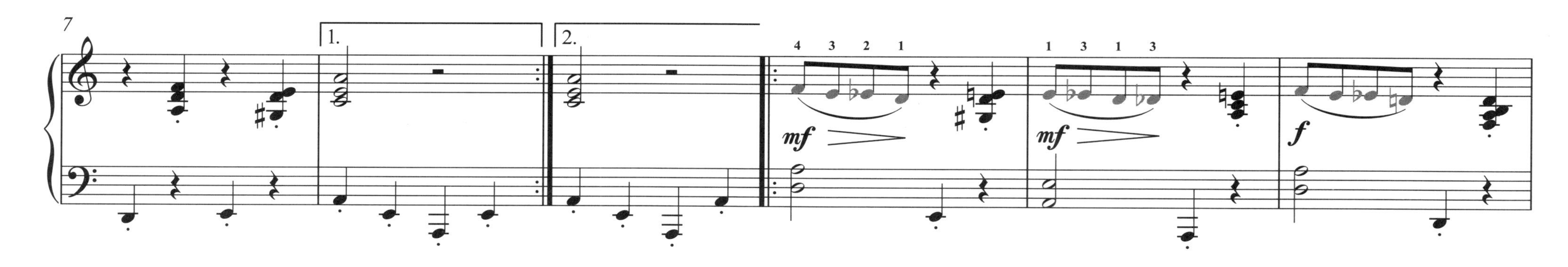

The Helter-Skelter

Hals über Kopf · À toutes jambes

Track 13/14

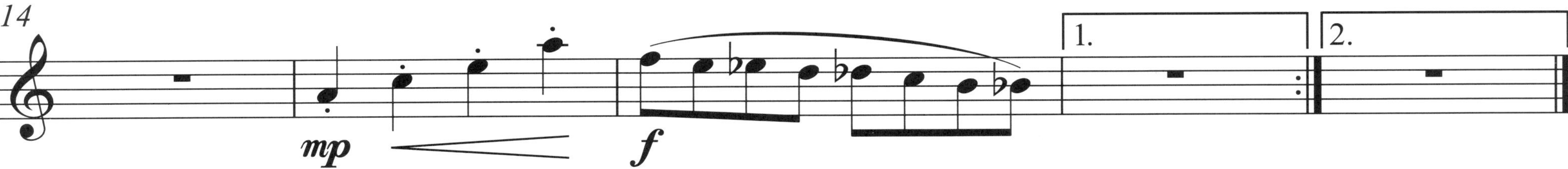

On the Ghost Train

Im Geisterzug · Le train fantôme

Track 15/16

On the Ghost Train

Im Geisterzug · Le train fantôme

Broken chords and chromatic phrases • *Dreiklangszerlegungen und chromatische Phrasen* • *Accords brisés et chromatisme*

The Donkey Ride

Der Eselsritt · Balade à dos d'âne

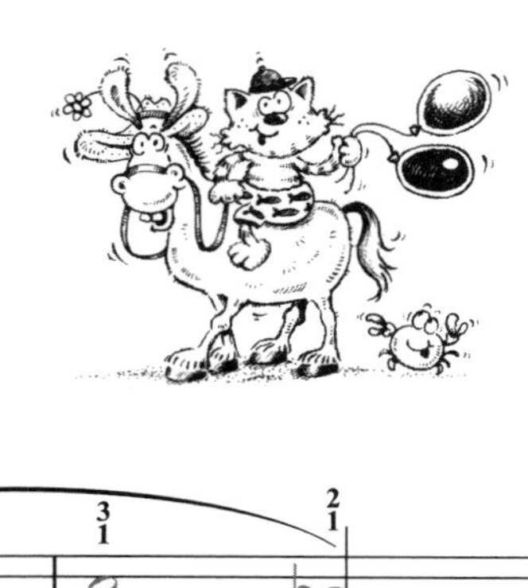

Legato Thirds • Legato Terzen • Tierces liées

The Donkey Ride

Der Eselsritt · Balade à dos d'âne

Track 17/18

The Deep Blue Sea

Das tiefblaue Meer · Profondeurs marine

Track 19/20

The Deep Blue Sea

Das tiefblaue Meer · Profondeurs marine

Legato Thirds • Legato Terzen • Tierces liées

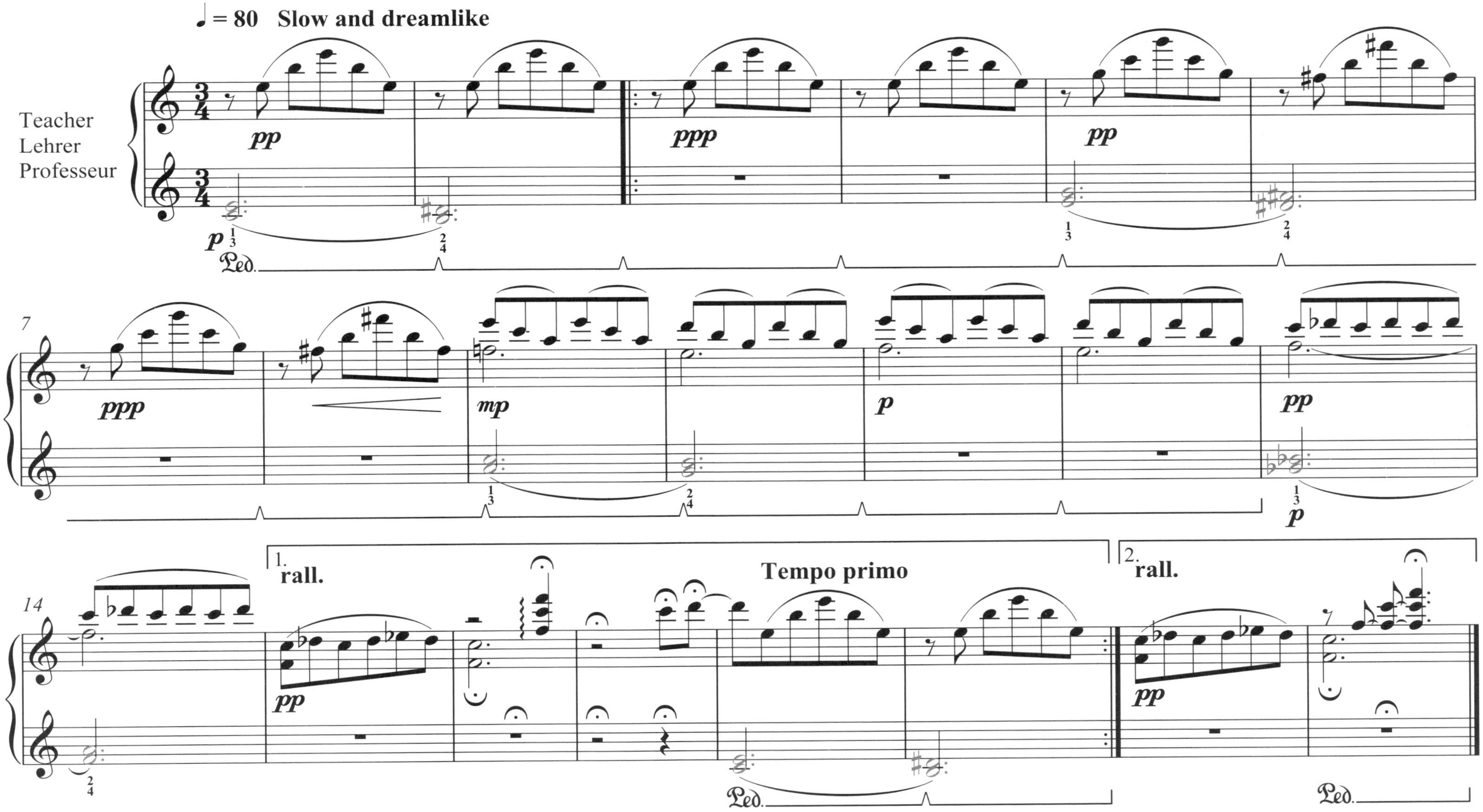

♩ = 80 **Slow and dreamlike**

Teacher
Lehrer
Professeur

pp p ppp pp ppp mp p pp p pp pp

1. rall. Tempo primo 2. rall.

On the Carousel

Auf dem Karussel · Tour de manège

Staccato Sixths • Staccato Sexten • Sixtes détachées

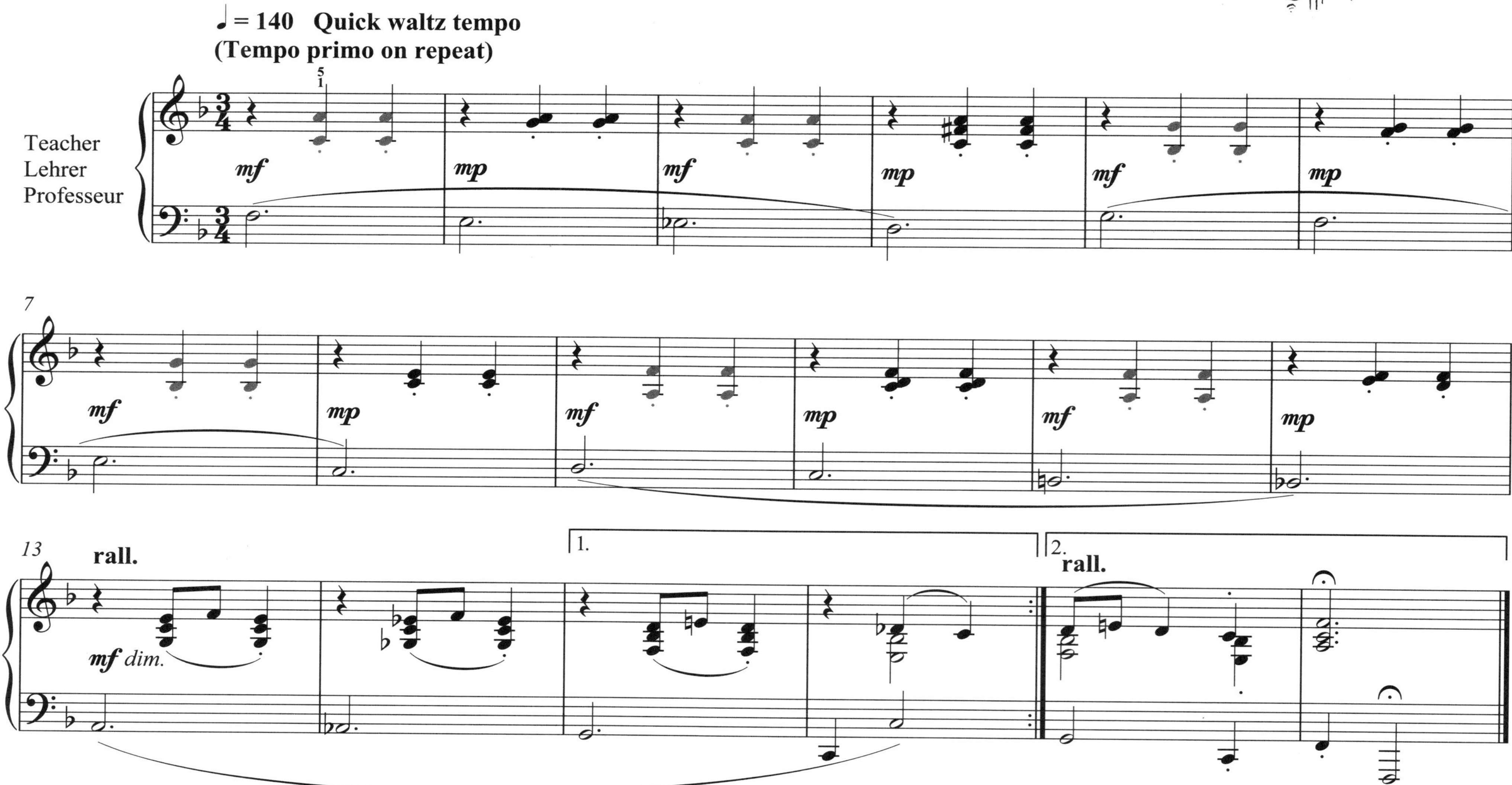

On the Carousel
Auf dem Karussel · Tour de manège
Track 21/22
♩ = 140 Quick waltz tempo
(Tempo primo on repeat)
Pupil
Schüler
Élève
mf
6
12
rall.
1.
2.
rall.

At the Aquarium

Beim Aquarium · Visite de l'aquarium

Track 23/24

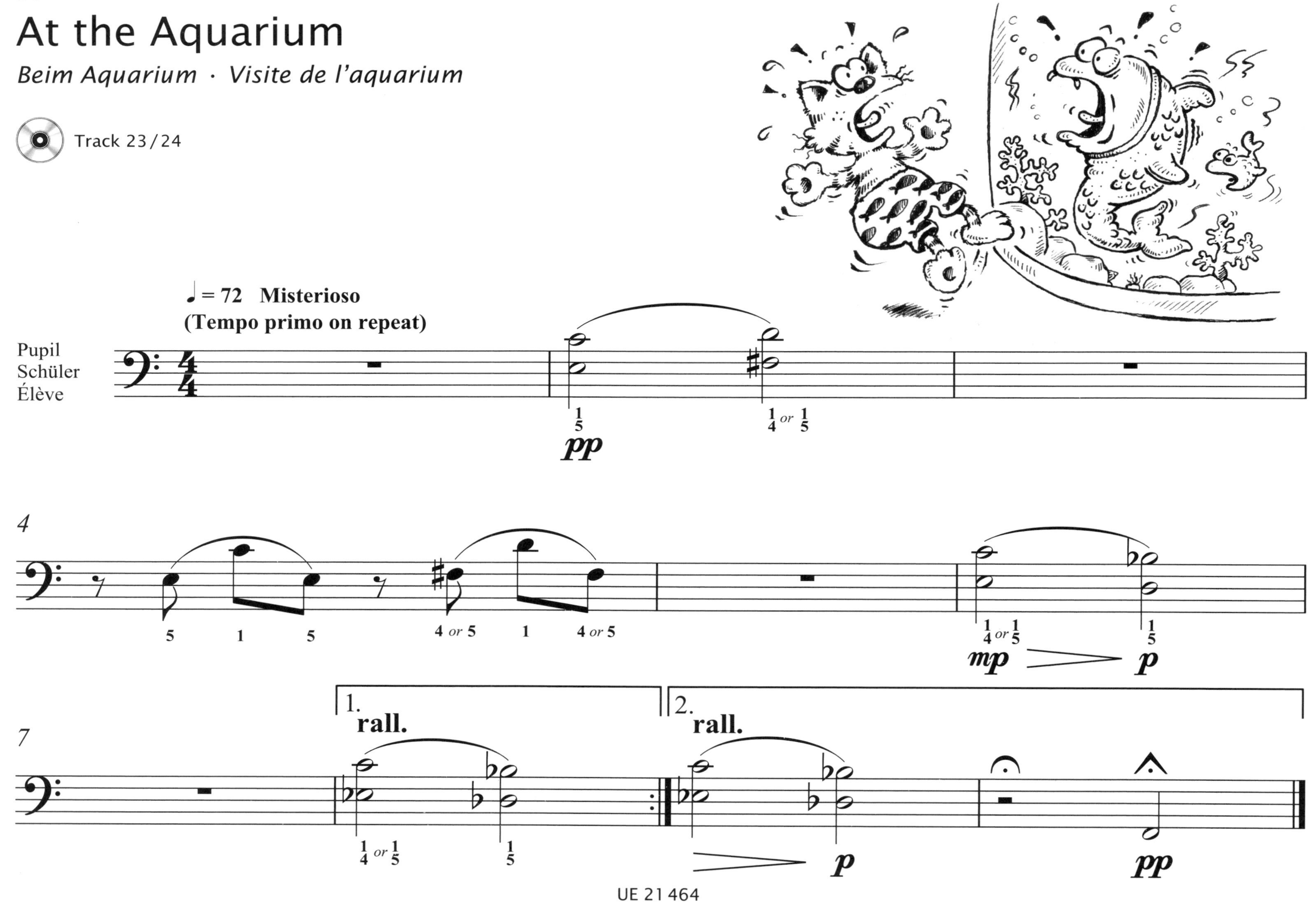

At the Aquarium

Beim Aquarium · Visite de l'aquarium

Legato Sixths • Legato Sexten • Sixtes liées

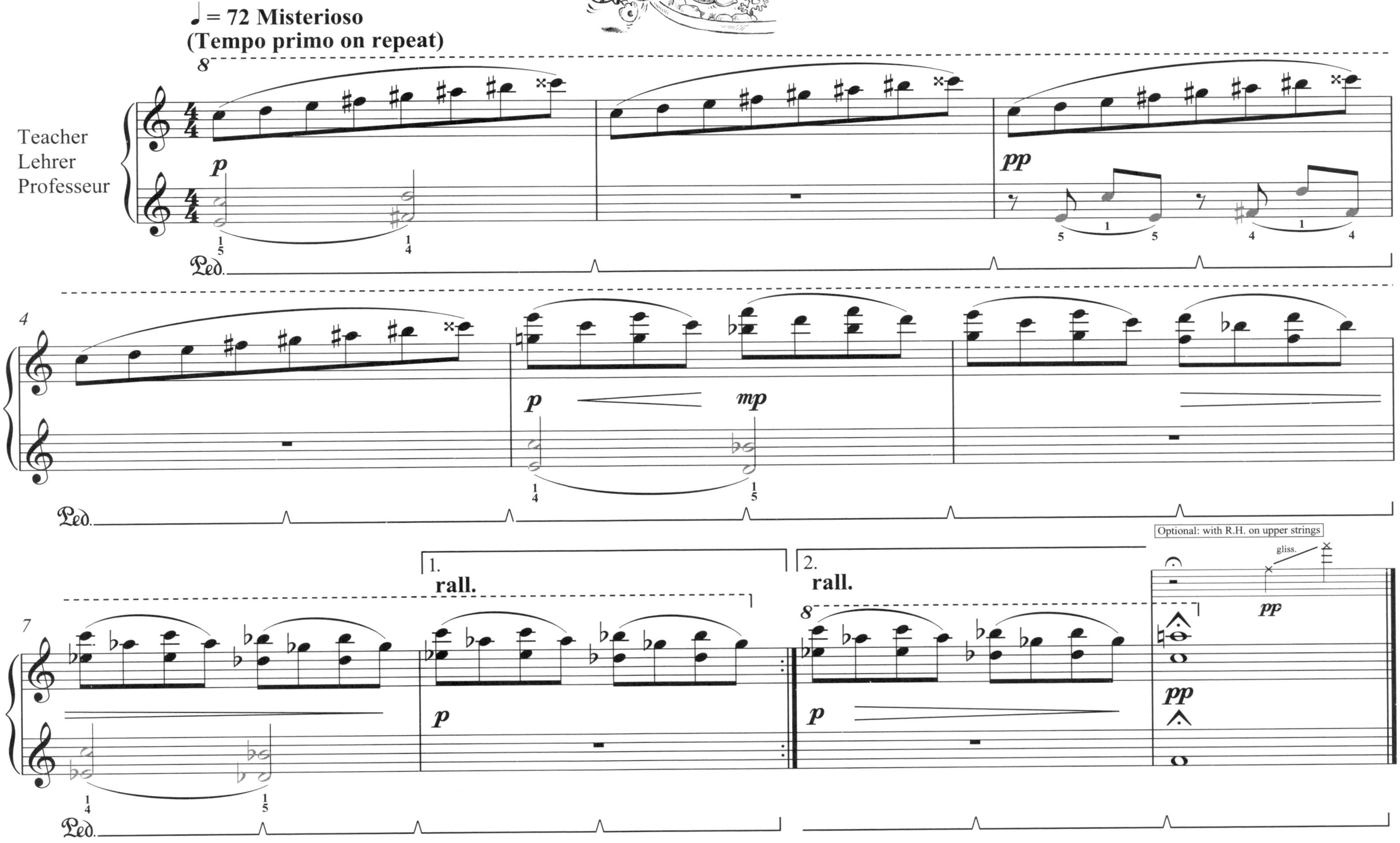

♩ = 72 Misterioso
(Tempo primo on repeat)

Teacher
Lehrer
Professeur

p pp p mp p rall. rall. p pp pp

Optional: with R.H. on upper strings

gliss.

The Echoing Caves

Das Höhlenecho · L'écho dans les grottes

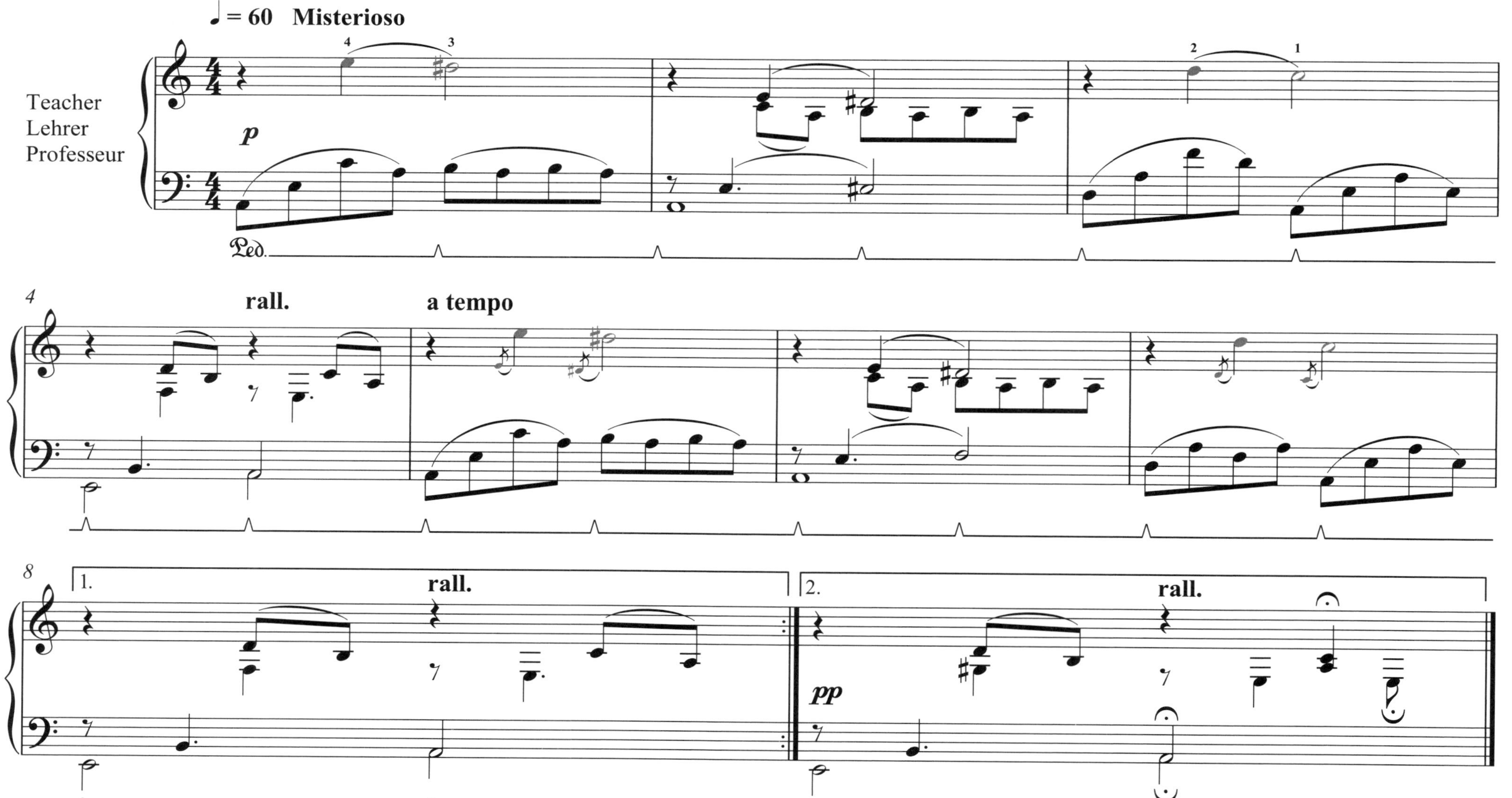

The Echoing Caves

Das Höhlenecho · L'écho dans les grottes

Track 25/26

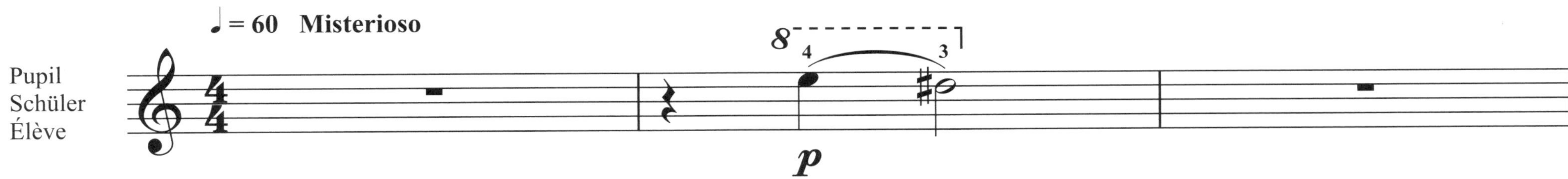

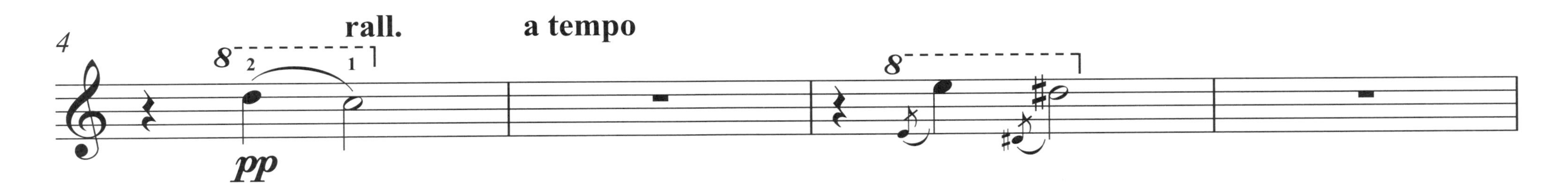

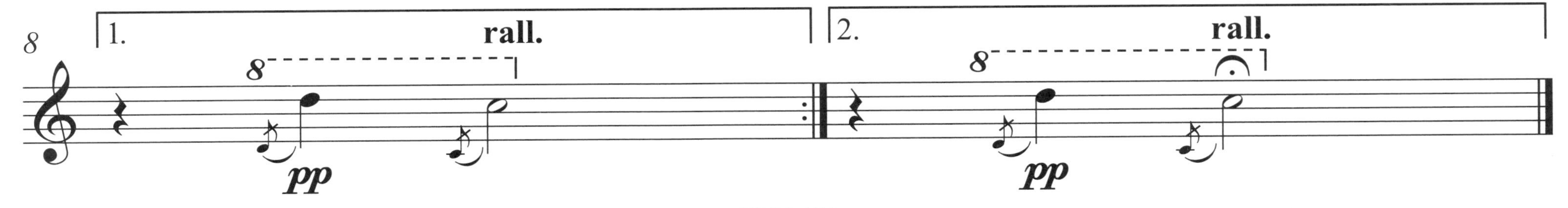

Into the Cold, Cold Waves

Hinein ins kalte Wasser! · Baignade en eaux froides

Track 27/28

Into the Cold, Cold Waves

Hinein ins kalte Wasser! · Baignade en eaux froides

Octaves • Oktaven • Octaves

♩ = 130 **Medium waltz tempo**

Teacher
Lehrer
Professeur

mp mf mp

Ped.

7

f mp f mp f

Ped. Ped. Ped.

13

1. 2.

f f

Ped. Ped.

Candy Floss 1

Zuckerwatte 1 · Barbe à papa 1

Candy Floss 1

Zuckerwatte 1 · Barbe à papa 1

Track 29/30

mf Can - dy floss, Pass some in my di - rec - tion! [*spoken: I'll love it!*]
Can - dy floss, Sticks to your paws and whis - kers! [*spoken: Alright then ...*]

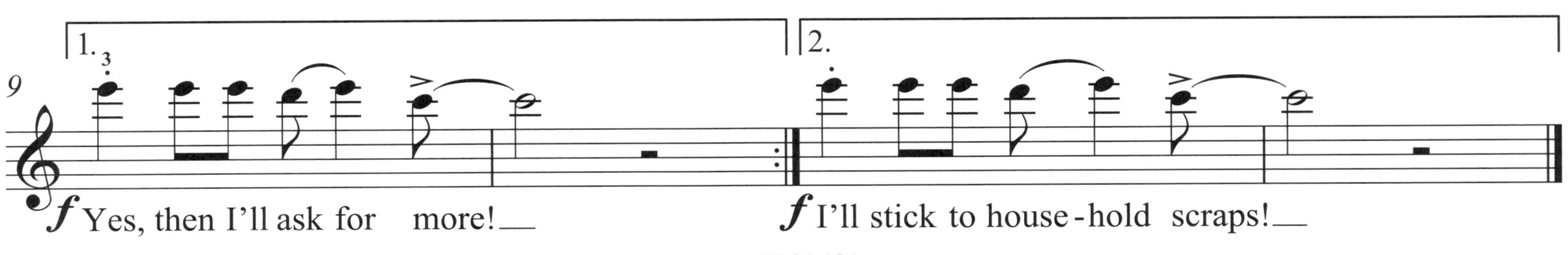

f Yes, then I'll ask for more!__

f I'll stick to house - hold scraps!__

Candy Floss 2

Zuckerwatte 2 · Barbe à papa 2

Track 31

Candy Floss 2

Zuckerwatte 2 · Barbe à papa 2

Candy Floss 3 – For the More Adventurous

Zuckerwatte 3 – Für die Mutigen · Barbe à papa 3 – Pour les plus courageux

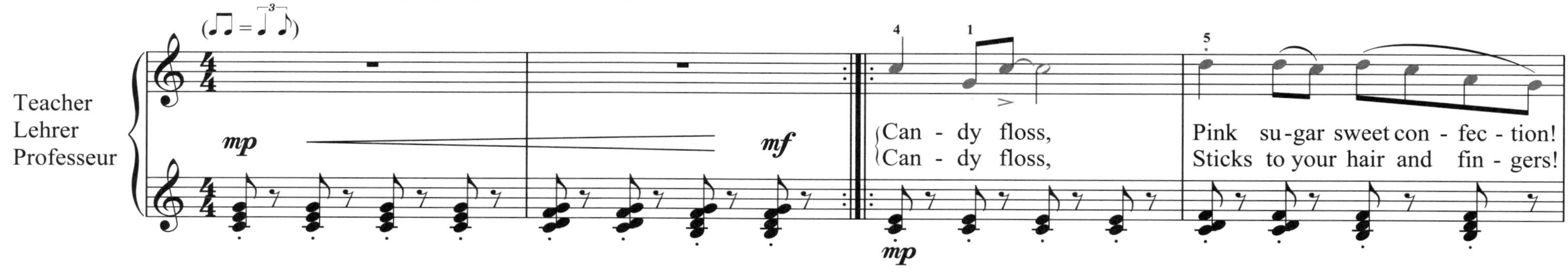

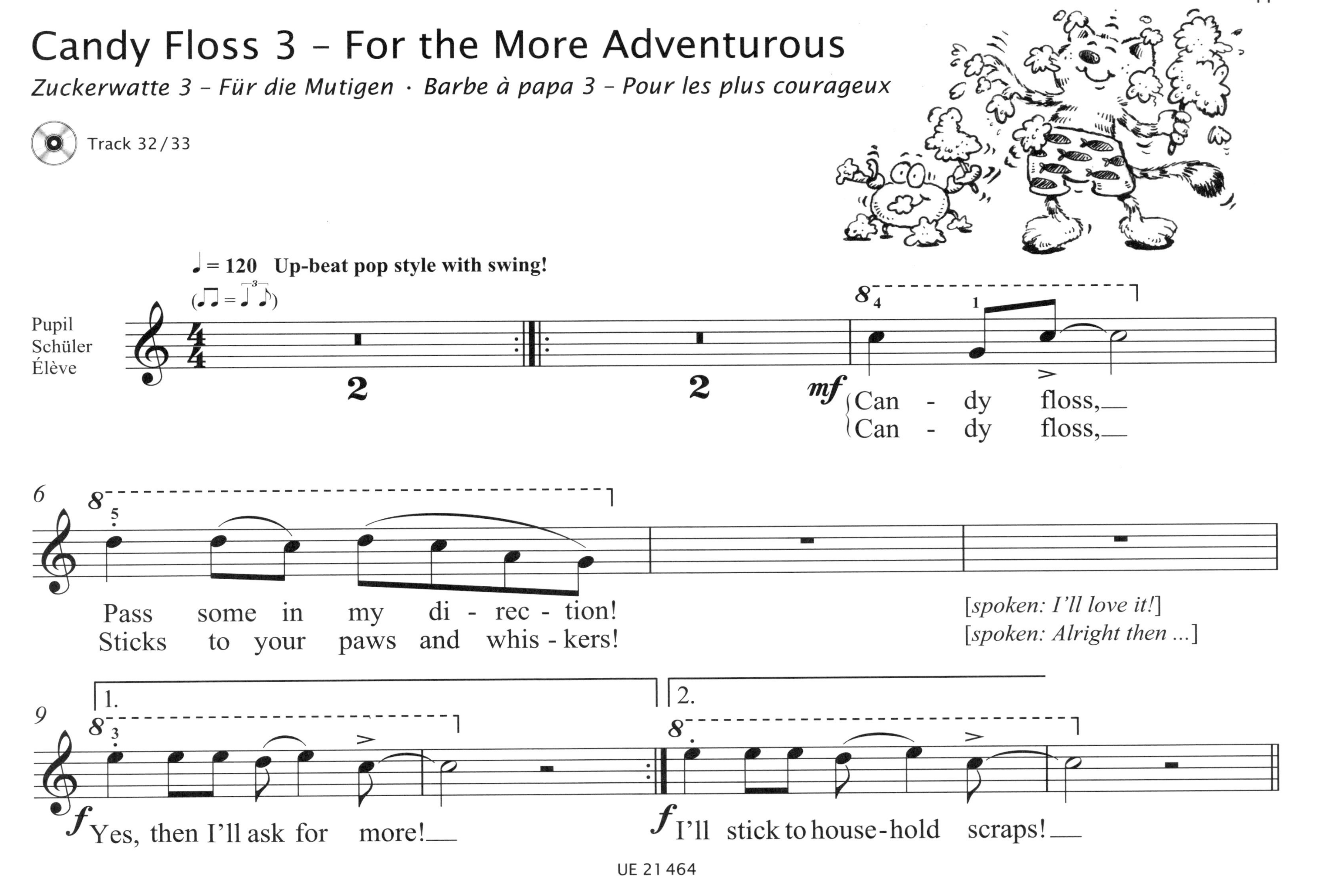
Candy Floss 3 – For the More Adventurous
Zuckerwatte 3 – Für die Mutigen · Barbe à papa 3 – Pour les plus courageux
Track 32/33
♩ = 120 Up-beat pop style with swing!
Pupil
Schüler
Élève
mf
Can - dy floss,
Can - dy floss,
Pass some in my di - rec - tion!
Sticks to your paws and whis - kers!
[spoken: I'll love it!]
[spoken: Alright then ...]
1.
2.
f
Yes, then I'll ask for more!
f
I'll stick to house-hold scraps!

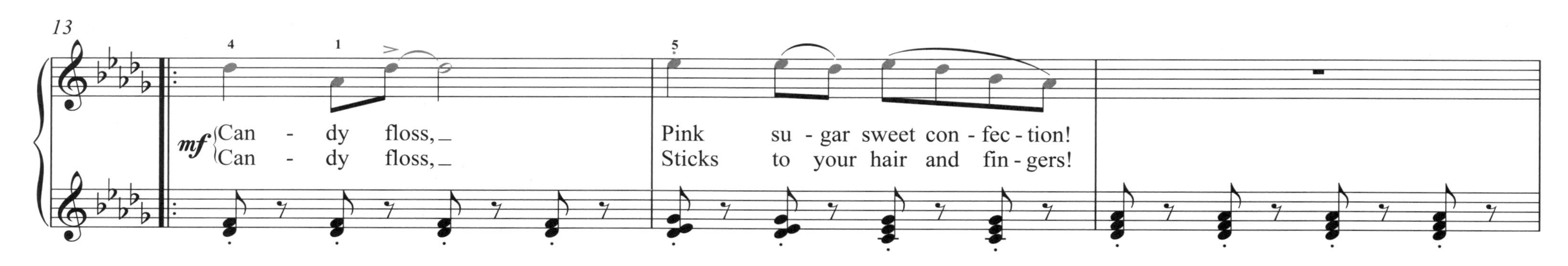
13
mf
Can - dy floss,
Can - dy floss,
Pink su - gar sweet con - fec - tion!
Sticks to your hair and fin - gers!

16
f
Think! Are you real - ly sure?
Not quite the food for cats!

19
1.
I doubt it!
2.

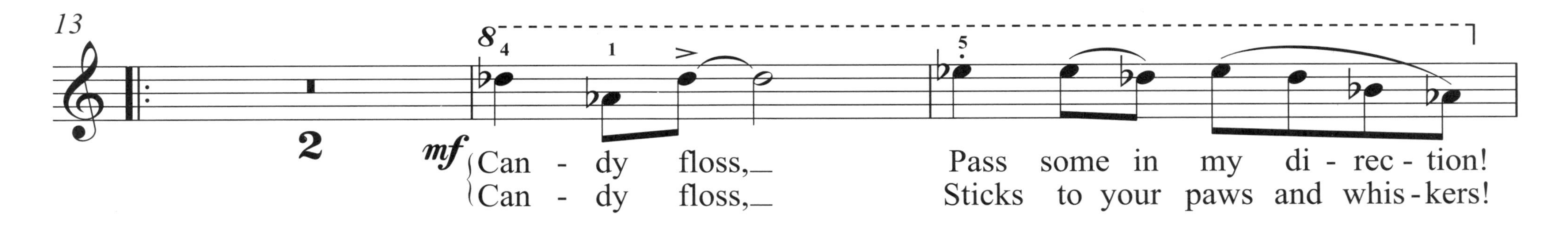
13
8
4
1
5
2
mf
Can - dy floss,
Can - dy floss,
Pass some in my di - rec - tion!
Sticks to your paws and whis - kers!

17
1.
8
3
[spoken: I'll love it!]
[spoken: Alright then ...]
f
Yes, then I'll ask for more!

21
2.
8
f
I'll stick to house - hold scraps!

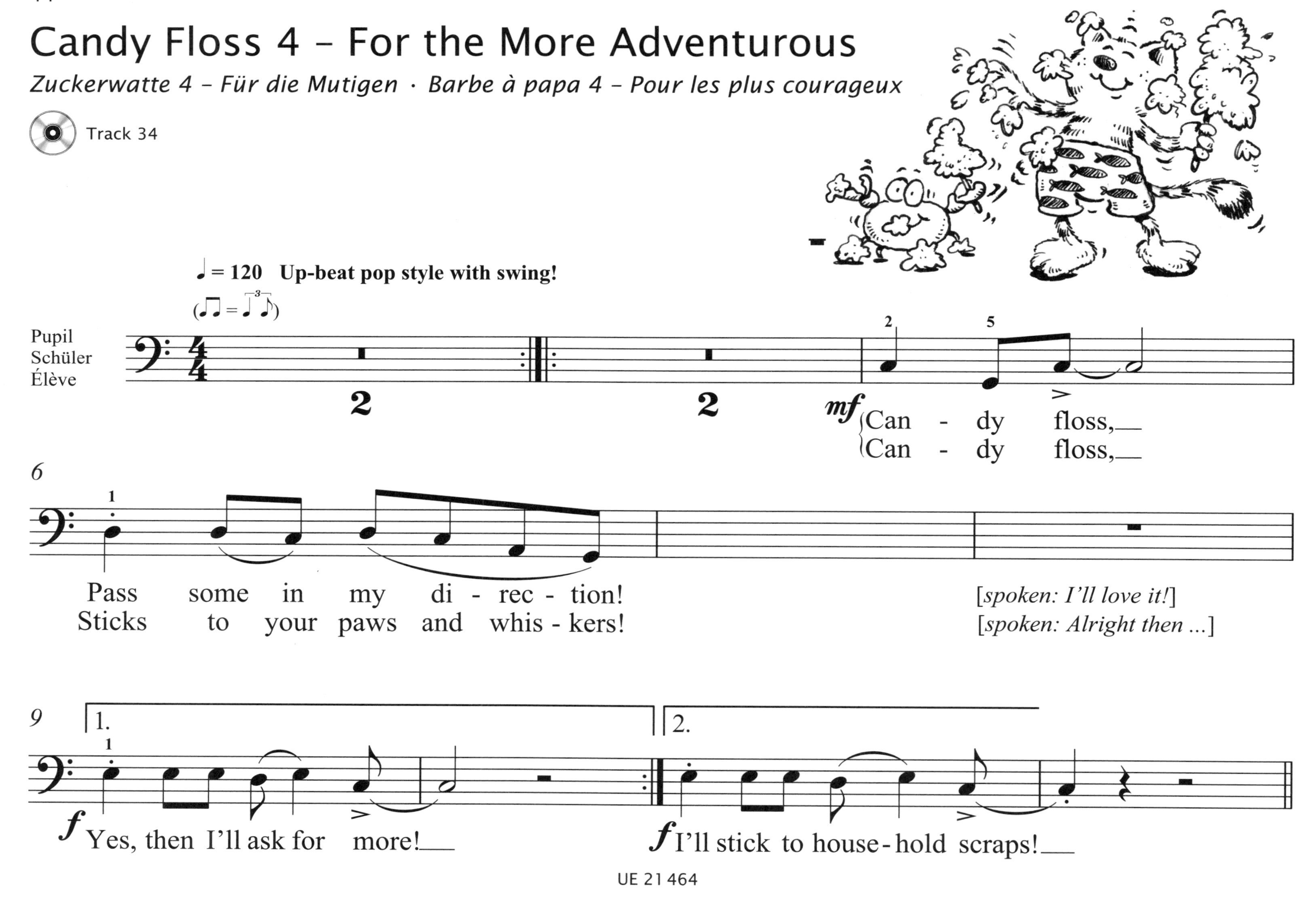
Candy Floss 4 – For the More Adventurous
Zuckerwatte 4 – Für die Mutigen · Barbe à papa 4 – Pour les plus courageux
Track 34
♩ = 120 Up-beat pop style with swing!
Pupil
Schüler
Élève
2
2
mf
Can - dy floss,
Can - dy floss,
6
Pass some in my di - rec - tion!
Sticks to your paws and whis - kers!
[spoken: I'll love it!]
[spoken: Alright then ...]
9
1.
2.
f
Yes, then I'll ask for more!
f
I'll stick to house - hold scraps!
UE 21 464

Candy Floss 4 – For the More Adventurous

Zuckerwatte 4 – Für die Mutigen · Barbe à papa 4 – Pour les plus courageux

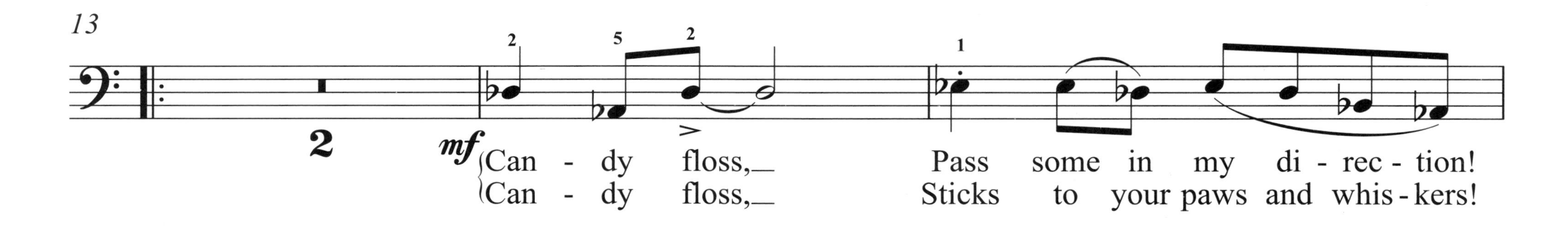
13
2
mf
Can - dy floss,
Pass some in my di - rec - tion!
Can - dy floss,
Sticks to your paws and whis - kers!

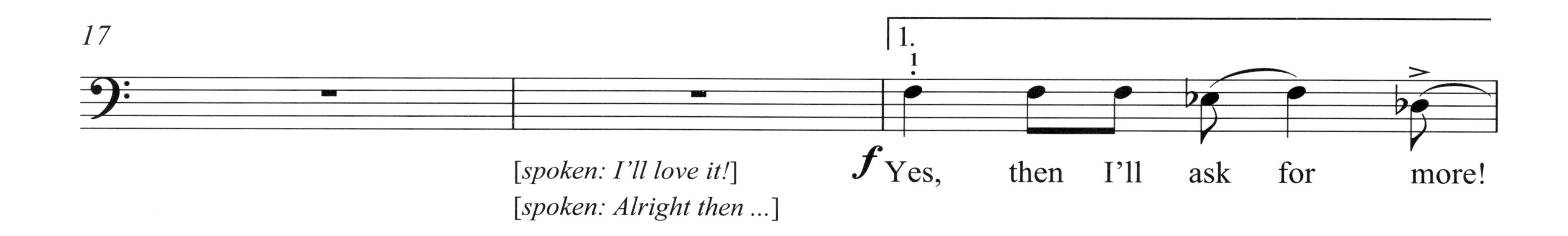
17
1.
[spoken: I'll love it!]
[spoken: Alright then ...]
f
Yes, then I'll ask for more!

20
2.
f
I'll stick to house-hold scraps!

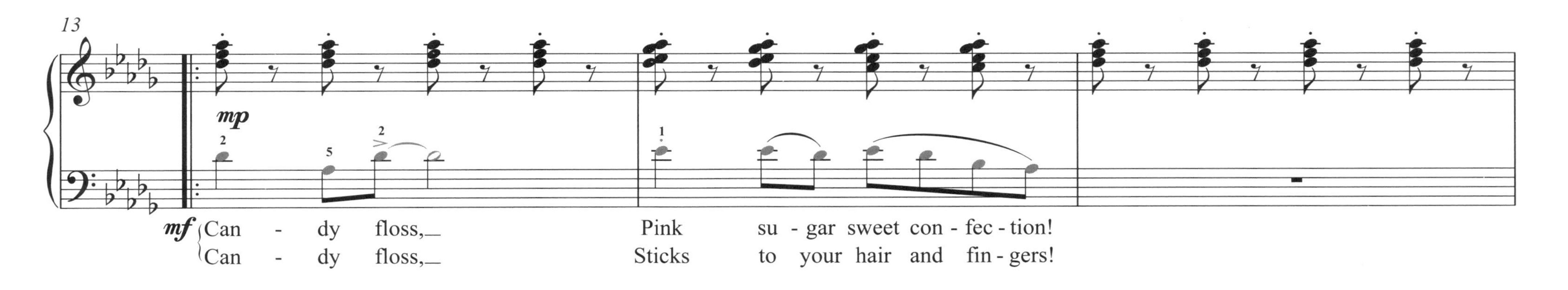
13
mp
mf
Can - dy floss,
Can - dy floss,
Pink su - gar sweet con - fec - tion!
Sticks to your hair and fin - gers!

16
mf
f
Think! Are you real - ly sure?
Not quite the food for cats!

19
1.
2.
f
I doubt it!

Dance of the Marionettes

Tanz der Marionetten · Danse des marionnettes

Dance of the Marionettes

Tanz der Marionetten · Danse des marionnettes

Track 35 / 36

Congratulations Clever Cat!

Clever Cat

by Mike Cornick

Teacher and beginner pupil piano duets with CD

The first book in the *Clever Cat* series. These duets are based on the simple idea of the pupil copying the teacher. They'll have young beginners happily playing with a real feeling of achievement – in their first lesson!

Together with *Clever Cat*, young players can have fun putting into practice the basic skills learnt during their first year of piano lessons.

- Amusing illustrations quickly remind pupils of the mood and varying styles of the pieces.
- There are opportunities for adding finger-clicks and vocal effects. e.g. *Caterwaulin'* includes 'miaows' for both pupil and teacher.
- A fun way of providing extra practice of five-finger exercises, scales, broken chords and arpeggios, which won't feel too much like hard work!
- The included CD contains performances of each duet and play-along tracks for pupils to use at home.

UE 21407

'... the pieces that followed [the preface] provided enjoyable extra practice for five-finger exercises, scales, broken chords and arpeggios in a variety of popular styles and managed to be wonderful performance pieces as well ... It is suitable for pupils in their first years ... but I also found it very useful for more advanced pupils whose musicianship skills and confidence needed a fun and pleasurable boost ... this book is unique ... thank you Mr Cornick!'

Fiona Lau, MUSIC TEACHER MAGAZINE

Clever Cat
Goes Solo

by Mike Cornick

for piano solo with CD

Following on from the teacher and pupil duet collections *Clever Cat* and *Clever Cat at the Seaside*, this set of pieces provides an opportunity for the young pianist to take flight on his or her own.

Working in a deliberately restricted range of keys, the pieces explore a variety of styles and feature quite specific pianistic skills.

e.g. *Chocks Away!* features thirds in the right hand, quaver triplets and the 12-bar blues chord sequence. *Looping the Loop* – 8va and loco instructions, the acciaccatura, changes in tempo and control of dynamics.

Other titles include: *Up, Up and Away, Touching the Clouds, Rollin' and a-Rockin', Gliding, The Parachutist* and *Coming in to Land.*

UE 21 484 – *Published July 2009*